The Hill

Pictures by Anne Davies with text by Danny Flynn

Pray for the hills that fall like flame
Pray for the landscape that sweeps a smile in both directions
Breathe for Mexico

Reza por las colinas que bajan como llama
Reza por el paisaje que barre una sonrisa en ambos direcciones
Respira por Mejico

Reza por las colinas

"What are you saying? Say something about me. Pray for me, and only me."

"¿Que estas diciendo? Di algo acerca de mi. Reza por mi, solo por mi."

On the other side of town

The hill had a fingerprint ploughed in the side

La colina tenia arada una nuella en el costado

The hill

The moon was a fingernail paring

La luna era una una cortadora

The moon

Buried in Mexico you were speaking with no beginning
Hidden in Mexico you were speaking with no beginning

Enterrada en Mejico hablabas sin un principio
Escondida en Mejico hablabas sin un principio

Limited to 48 copies

1999

Burning Book Press